Flopsy

Tom Tierney

PLATE 1: FLOPSY

Flopsy is a well-behaved little kitten who likes to keep her white paws
and bib spanking clean.

Mopsy

Tom Tierney

PLATE 2: MOPSY

Mopsy's big blue eyes reveal her curiosity about everything, from butterflies to sunflowers.

Max

PLATE 3: MAX

Max is a mischievous fellow who likes to romp and play and behave like a clown.

Auntie Tabitha

PLATE 4: AUNTIE TABITHA

Auntie Tabitha is the kittens' "nanny." She takes them on both short trips and longer excursions. She always carries a few spears of catnip in her apron pocket, a reward for the kittens when they behave themselves.

PLATE 5: THE SUNDAY TEA PARTY

On Sunday afternoons the kittens get dressed up for a catnip tea party in the garden. Flopsy's pretty pink print calico party frock makes her feel very special.

PLATE 6: THE SUNDAY TEA PARTY

Mopsy just can't resist picking some of the flowers in the garden. She has decorated her cap with a chain of yellow posies.

PLATE 7: THE SUNDAY TEA PARTY

Max says he doesn't like tea parties very much, but he looks quite dapper
in his "ice cream" skimmer.

PLATE 8: A SUMMER OUTING

Sometimes Nanny takes her charges to the park for an outing. Flopsy and the other kittens usually dress up for these occasions because Nanny says that you never know whom you might meet while strolling in the park.

PLATE 9: A SUMMER OUTING

What Mopsy likes best about the park is that you can buy a balloon. She
can spend many pleasant hours bouncing it about.

PLATE 10: A SUMMER OUTING

Although Max would rather be wearing coveralls, he is still having a good time, especially bird-watching!

PLATE 11: A COUNTRY HOLIDAY

Every once in a while, Nanny takes the kittens with her to visit an old friend who lives in the country. Flopsy wears a bonnet to keep the sun out of her eyes.

PLATE 12: A COUNTRY HOLIDAY

Mopsy likes to pick flowers on her country holiday. She wears an apron to protect her pretty checked gingham dress.

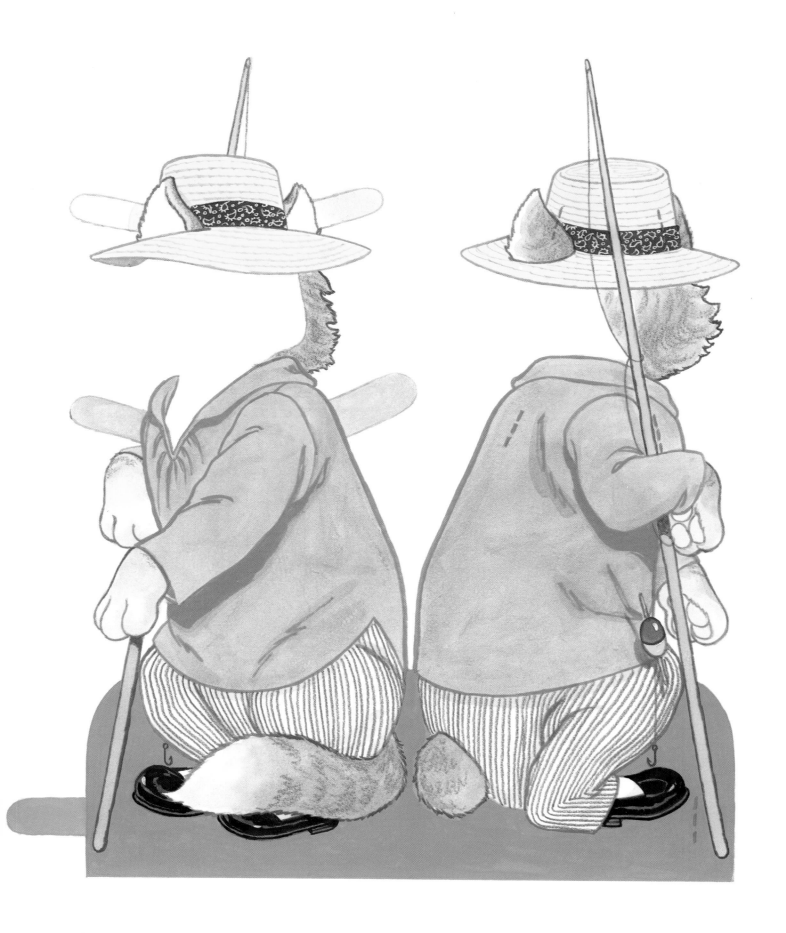

PLATE 13: A COUNTRY HOLIDAY

Max is a good fisherman and spends most of his holiday fishing at the pond.

PLATE 14: "PUSS IN BOOTS"

Nanny taught the kittens to recite drama and poetry, so when their school put on a play about Puss in Boots, they were all chosen for parts. Flopsy plays a queen.

PLATE 15: "PUSS IN BOOTS"

Mopsy was chosen to play a beautiful princess who falls in love with Puss.

PLATE 16: "PUSS IN BOOTS"

Max, of course, plays Puss, the hero. His swashbuckling behavior on stage is most impressive.